Core Knowledge Language Arts®

Unit 6
Workbook

Skills Strand
GRADE 1

Amplify learning.

Core Knowledge®

Unit 6
Workbook

This Workbook contains worksheets that accompany many of the lessons from the *Teacher Guide* for Unit 6. Each worksheet is identified by the lesson number in which it is used. Some of the worksheets in this book do not include written instructions for students because the instructions would have contained nondecodable words. The expectation is that teachers will explain these worksheets to students orally, using the guidelines in the Teacher Guide. Nondecodable instructions are also included along the side of each of these worksheets, and are only meant to be read aloud by a teacher or family member. The Workbook is a student component, which means each student should have a Workbook.

Dear Family Member,

Today our class started Unit 6 of the Core Knowledge Language Arts program. The reader for this unit is called *Grace*. Your child will bring home stories you can read together about Grace and her life on a farm. Remember that reading at home with your child is important for their success as a reader.

In addition, your child's spelling words for this week include a review of previously taught sound-spellings. As usual, there is one Tricky Word. Tricky Words do not play by the rules, meaning there are spellings that do not sound the way students would expect them to. Tricky Words need to be memorized, so your child will benefit from practice reading and writing them.

Spelling Words

1. swimming

2. rotten

3. hidden

4. batter

5. shredded

6. popping

7. nodded

8. Tricky Word: their

In the Cave

When I went to visit with Nan, I was sad. I missed Mom and Dad. But Nan cheered me up and made things fun.

Nan took me on hikes. The land I saw in the West was not at all like the land I am used to. Where I am from, things are green in the summer, and there are lots of trees. In the West, there are hills and red rocks, but not a lot of trees. In some spots, you can hike for a mile and not see one tree!

<u>Once</u>, Nan and I were on a hike when it started to storm. Nan and I went into a cave so that we would not get wet.

As we were standing there, I saw something shimmer in the dark.

"Nan," I said, pointing at the spot, "what's that?"

"Well," said Nan, "let's have a look."

We looked and saw something stuck in a crack in the rock. I grabbed it.

"It's a coin!" I said.

"Well, I'll be!" said Nan.

I said, "What sort of coin is it?"

Nan said, "I can't tell. It looks like it c<u>ou</u>ld be made of silver."

Then she said, "I have a pal, Jack, who is an expert on coins. We can bring it to him tom<u>orrow</u>, and he will tell us what sort of coin it is."

I dropped the coin in my pocket, and we went on with our hike.

4 *Unit 6*

The Name of the Tale:

Directions: Have students fill in the story map to describe the characters, setting, and plot of the story.

Who?

Where? When?

What?

The tale starts with . . .

Next in the tale . . .

At the end of the tale . . .

Sound out the words with the lines under them. Is the 'c' sounded /k/ as in *cat* or /s/ as in *cent*? Write the words where they fit best.

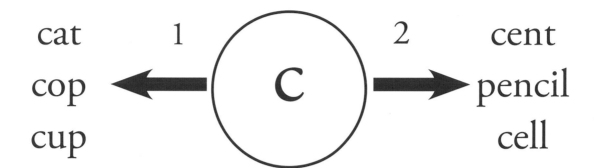

	/k/ as in *cat*	/s/ as in *cent*
1. She is a good dan<u>c</u>er.		dancer
2. It's time to get in the <u>c</u>ar.		
3. That kite you have is so <u>c</u>ool!		
4. Set it down in the <u>c</u>enter of the room.		
5. For lunch we had <u>c</u>rabs.		
6. He gave me a lot of choi<u>c</u>es.		
7. Look up there! See that big <u>c</u>loud?		

Dear Family Member,

We have been working on writing personal narratives at school. Your child has read personal narratives and we have drafted a personal narrative as a class. Now, each student will have an opportunity to write his or her own personal narrative describing something that has happened to him or her. As homework, please work with your child to brainstorm ideas that he or she might write about in a personal narrative. Remind your child that the personal narrative should tell about something that has really happened to him or her. Here are some ideas for topics your child might be interested in writing about:

- a special holiday or birthday
- a special present they received
- something a friend or sibling did for them
- a special visit or a trip to an interesting place
- a "first" or significant personal achievement
- a weather-related event

Have your child jot down ideas on the back of this page to bring back to school tomorrow.

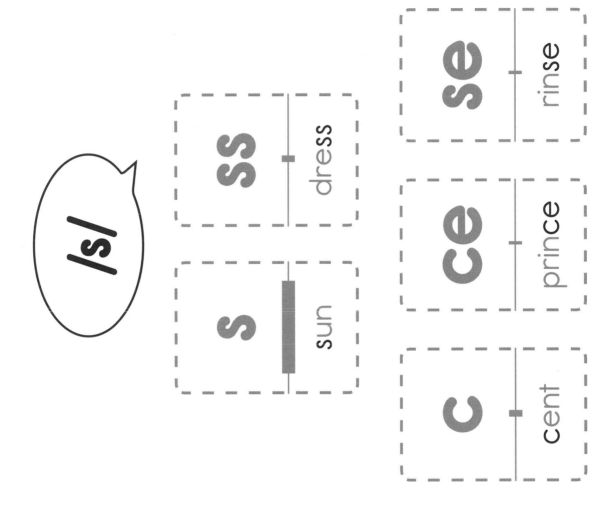

/s/

ss — dress

s — sun

se — rinse

ce — prince

c — cent

Plan a Tale That Happened to You

 Who?	Who was in the tale? Describe them.
 Where?  When?	Where and when did the tale take place? Describe the setting.
 What?	What happened at the start? What happened next? What happened after that? What happened last? Describe all parts of the tale.
 Why?	Why did this happen? Why was this important?

Draft a Tale That Happened to You

Who is in the tale?

Where did the tale
take place?

When did the tale
take place?

What happened at
the start?
What happened
next?
What happened
after that?
What happened last?

Why did this
happen?

Sort the words by their spellings for /s/.

prin**ce**	hor**se**	sin**ce**	rin**se**	choi**ce**
fen**ce**	dan**ce**	hou**se**	mou**se**	goo**se**

/s/ → 'ce'

_____

- - - - - - - - - - - - - - - - -

_____

- - - - - - - - - - - - - - - - -

_____

- - - - - - - - - - - - - - - - -

_____

- - - - - - - - - - - - - - - - -

_____

- - - - - - - - - - - - - - - - -

_____

/s/ → 'se'

_____

- - - - - - - - - - - - - - - - -

_____

- - - - - - - - - - - - - - - - -

_____

- - - - - - - - - - - - - - - - -

_____

- - - - - - - - - - - - - - - - -

_____

- - - - - - - - - - - - - - - - -

_____

Spelling Test

1. _____

2. _____

3. _____

4. _____

5. _____

6. _____

7. _____

8. _____

Check the Draft
Step by Step

1. Check that you described who was in the tale.	
2. Check that you described where the tale took place.	
3. Check that you described when the tale took place.	
4. Check that you described what happened in the tale in order from start to finish.	
5. Check that you described why the tale happened or why it was important.	
6. Aa, Bb, Cc	
7. ? . !	
8. Check that the words are spelled well.	

Name _____

Dear Family Member,

Our class has been learning spelling alternatives for the /s/ sound. The /s/ sound can be written with the spellings 's', 'ss', 'c', 'ce', and 'se'. The spelling words this week contain these spellings for /s/, as well as spellings for its buzzy sister sound, /z/. The /z/ sound can be written with the spellings 'z', 'zz', and 's'.

As usual, there is one Tricky Word. Tricky Words do not play by the rules, meaning there are spellings that do not sound the way students would expect them to. Tricky Words need to be memorized, so your child will benefit from practice reading and writing them.

Spelling Words

1. sun

2. kiss

3. cent

4. prince

5. jazz

6. pigs

7. zip

8. Tricky Word: here

/s/ and /k/ spelled 'c'

Directions: Have students color the boxes that contain words that have 'c' > /k/ as in cat in one color and the boxes that contain words that have 'c' > /s/ as in cent in another color.

clip	pencil	carve
cells	cage	bouncing
cent	center	bobcat
catch	dancer	magic

Cut out the word cards and stick them on the next sheet.

cell	**c**enter
voi**ce**	prin**ce**
twi**ce**	el**se**
den**se**	chan**ce**
hou**se**	hor**se**
per**c**ent	dan**c**ing

Sort the word cards by their spellings for /s/ and stick them in the boxes.

/s/ → 'se'						
/s/ → 'c' or 'ce'						

Mister Spencer and the Rabbits

1. What is the land like out in the Midwest?

    ○   The land has red rocks.

    ○   The land has no plants.

    ○   The land has rich soil.

Page _____

2. What things are in Mister Spencer's garden?

_____

_____

_____

_____

Page _____

3. What is the problem with Mister Spencer's garden?

   ○ He has rabbits in his garden.

   ○ He has a dog in his garden.

   ○ He has sprouts in his garden.

Page _____

4. Pepper helps Mister Spencer when he . . .

   ○ has a snack from the garden.

   ○ barks at the rabbits so they run off.

   ○ sleeps out in the barn.

Page _____

Directions: Have students underline the pronouns and draw a connecting line from each pronoun to the noun it replaces. Then have students write the pronoun on the line below.

1. Kate is nine. <u>She</u> wrote a book.

2. Jack has a shop. He sells coins.

3. Kate went on a trip. It was fun.

4. Kate found a coin. It is Spanish.

1. <u>Kate</u> went on a trip. She had fun.

2. Jack likes the <u>coin</u>. Jack likes _____.

3. Was <u>Jack</u> Nan's pal? Yes, _____ was Nan's pal.

4. <u>Kate</u> made a book. _____ wrote the words.

5. Nan has a <u>cabin</u>. _____ is in the West.

6. <u>Max</u> is a kid. _____ is nine.

Directions: Have students replace the underlined nouns with the proper pronouns, using he, she, or it.

Dear Family Member,

This is a story your child has probably read once, possibly several times, at school. Encourage your child to read the story to you and then talk about it together. The tricky parts in Tricky Words are underlined in gray.

Repeated oral reading is an important way to improve reading skills. It can be fun for your child to repeatedly read this story to a friend, relative, or even a pet.

Mister Spencer and the Rabbits

Grace Spencer's dad has a farm. Her dad is a farmer out in the Midwest, where the land is flat and the soil is rich.

In the spring Mister Spencer plants corn next to the farmhouse. All summer long, he takes care of the corn. By the end of the summer, the corn is ripe. Then Mister Spencer harvests it and sells it. That is how he makes a living.

Mister Spencer has a garden, too. In his garden he plants eggplants, beets, sprouts, and peppers.

Mister Spencer has had some problems with rabbits. They crawl under the fence, hop into his garden, and munch on his plants. When Mister Spencer sees the rabbits in his garden, he gets mad as a hornet. He shakes his fist and shouts at the rabbits.

Grace and her sister Jill like the rabbits. Grace says they are cute. She tells her dad to be nice and let the rabbits be. But Mister Spencer can't stand those rabbits, and the Spencers need the plants in the garden to feed them in the winter.

Last summer, Mister Spencer got a dog to force the rabbits out of his garden. The dog's name is Pepper. He is a black dog. He sleeps out in the barn.

When Pepper came to the farm, he gave the rabbits quite a scare. They were in the garden, munching on sprouts. Then Pepper came charging out into the yard, barking. The rabbits took off! They raced back into their hole as fast as they could.

Pepper ran to the rabbit hole and went in as far as he could. He started digging with his paws. But it was no use. It was a deep hole and he could not get down to where the rabbits were.

Mister Spencer was sitting in the living room at the time. He could tell what Pepper was up to. He smiled. "Good dog!" he said. "Good dog! I bet those rabbits will munch on sprouts somewhere else next time!"

The Picnic by the River

1. What was in the picnic basket?

    _____

    _____

    _____

    _____

    _____

    Page _____

2. Where had the Spencers set d<u>ow</u>n th<u>eir</u> picnic basket?

    _____

    _____

    _____

    _____

    Page _____

3. Why was the food in the picnic basket safe from the ants?

_____

_____

_____

_____

Page _____

4. What did Grace do for the ants at the end?

_____

_____

_____

_____

Page _____

he   she   it   I   you

1. The hou**se** is big. <u>It</u> has lots of rooms.

2. Mitch has a black goo**se**. He likes the goo**se**.

3. Ben said, "I have lots of red pen**c**ils."

4. Mom asked Ree**se**, "Can you feed the hor**se**?"

5. The prin**c**ess broke her leg. She has to use crutches.

6. The mou**se** is soft. It is a ni**c**e mou**se**.

Directions: Have students underline the pronoun in each sentence pair and draw a connecting line from the pronoun to the noun it replaces. Then have students write the pronoun on the line.

Ants

Directions: Have students reread the story and answer the questions.

1. What is an ant farm?

    _____

    - - - - - - - - - - - - - - - - - - -

    _____

    - - - - - - - - - - - - - - - - - - -

    _____

    - - - - - - - - - - - - - - - - - - -

    _____

    - - - - - - - - - - - - - - - - - - -

    Page _____

2. Who is the queen?

    Page _____

3. How do the rest of the ants take care of the queen?

_____

- -

_____

_____

- -

_____

_____

- -

_____

_____

- -

_____

Page _____

4. Why could the queen's life be a hard life?

_____

- -

_____

_____

- -

_____

_____

- -

_____

_____

- -

_____

Page _____

1. choice

2. cent

3. glance

4. grouse

5. house

6. cells

7. prince

8. center

Spelling Test

1. _____

2. _____

3. _____

4. _____

5. _____

6. _____

7. _____

8. _____

Name _____

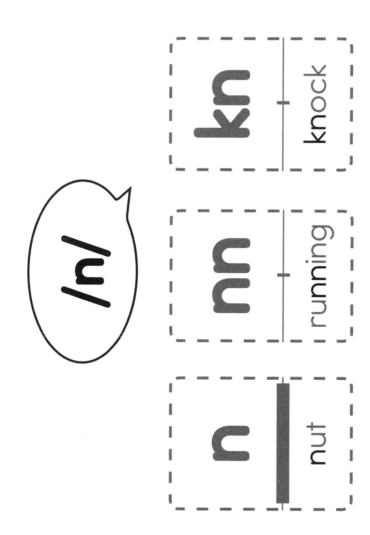

The Band

1. What did Grace and Jill sound like at the start?

_____
- - - - - - - - - - - - - - - - - -
_____
- - - - - - - - - - - - - - - - - -
_____
- - - - - - - - - - - - - - - - - -
_____

Page _____

2. How did Mister Spencer act when the children started out?

_____
- - - - - - - - - - - - - - - - - -
_____
- - - - - - - - - - - - - - - - - -
_____
- - - - - - - - - - - - - - - - - -
_____

Page _____

Directions: Have students reread the story and answer the questions.

3. Who is Mister Van**ce**?

_____

- - - - - - - - - - - - - - - - - -

_____

- - - - - - - - - - - - - - - - - -

_____

- - - - - - - - - - - - - - - - - -

_____

- - - - - - - - - - - - - - - - - -

Page _____

4. Describe the band con**c**ert.

_____

- - - - - - - - - - - - - - - - - -

_____

- - - - - - - - - - - - - - - - - -

_____

- - - - - - - - - - - - - - - - - -

_____

- - - - - - - - - - - - - - - - - -

Page _____

Name _____

Sort the words by their spellings for /s/.

sit	grass	dress	snake	hips
cell	sun	center	cent	kiss

/s/ → 's'

/s/ → 'ss'

/s/ → 'c'

Dear Family Member,

Your child's spelling words for this week include a review of previously taught sound-spellings. As usual, there is one Tricky Word. Tricky Words do not play by the rules, meaning there are spellings that do not sound the way students would expect them to. These words need to be memorized, so your child will benefit from practice reading and writing them.

Spelling Words

1. maps

2. mice

3. hammer

4. trimmed

5. skipped

6. scrub

7. space

8. Tricky Word: could

Sort the words by their spellings for /n/.

| sense | knit | dinner | knee | nerve |
| running | winner | cent | knot | fence |

/n/ → 'n'	/n/ → 'nn'	/n/ → 'kn'

Can you see the spelling pattern? Fill in the chart.

Root Word	–ed Word	–ing Word
tan	tanned	tanning
grin		
plan		
scan		

Write the words on the correct lines.

cent	goose	fence
knot	mouse	prince
dance	knee	moose

_____

_____

_____

_____

_____

_____

_____

_____

_____

The Yard Sale

Directions: Have students reread the story and answer the questions.

1. What is for sale at the yard sale?

   _____
   -
   _____
   -
   _____
   -
   _____
   -
   _____

   Page _____

2. What is Grace's problem?

   _____
   -
   _____
   -
   _____
   -
   _____
   -
   _____

   Page _____

3. How was Grace's problem solved?

_____

Page _____

4. Why did the man let Grace get two books for the price of one?

_____

Page _____

The Storm

1. Describe the storm on the farm.

    _____
    -
    _____
    _____
    -
    _____
    _____
    -
    _____
    _____
    -
    _____

    Page _____

2. Did Grace like the storm?

    _____
    -
    _____
    _____
    -
    _____
    _____
    -
    _____
    _____
    -
    _____

    Page _____

Directions: Have students reread the story and answer the questions.

3. Did Jill like the storm?

Page _____

4. What did Grace tell Jill to make her feel better?

Page _____

He	**She**	**It**

1. <u>Vin**ce**</u> is a good catcher.

2. <u>The mou**se**</u> is on the fen**ce**.

3. <u>The prin**ce**</u> had goo**se** for dinner.

4. <u>The hor**se**</u> ran in a race.

5. <u>Mom</u> has a red blou**se**.

6. <u>Gran **kn**</u>its socks for her grandkids.

Dark Clouds and Wind

Directions: Have students reread the story and answer the questions.

1. What did Mister Spencer see as they finished up lunch?

    _____

    -

    _____

    -

    _____

    -

    _____

    Page _____

2. What do the Spencers do when the clouds get darker and the wind picks up?

    _____

    -

    _____

    -

    _____

    -

    _____

    Page _____

3. What is a storm shelter?

_____

- - - - - - - - - - - - - - - - - - - -

_____

- - - - - - - - - - - - - - - - - - - -

_____

- - - - - - - - - - - - - - - - - - - -

_____

- - - - - - - - - - - - - - - - - - - -

_____

Page _____

4. What did Grace shout as Mister Spencer started to lock up the shutters?

_____

- - - - - - - - - - - - - - - - - - - -

_____

- - - - - - - - - - - - - - - - - - - -

_____

- - - - - - - - - - - - - - - - - - - -

_____

- - - - - - - - - - - - - - - - - - - -

_____

Page _____

Name _____

Dear Family Member,

This is a story your child has probably read once, possibly several times, at school. Encourage your child to read the story to you and then talk about it together.

Repeated oral reading is an important way to improve reading skills. It can be fun for your child to repeatedly read this story to a friend, relative, or even a pet.

The Band

Gra**ce** and Jill are in a band. Gra**ce** toots on her trumpet. Jill toots on her slide trombone.

When the children started out, they did not sound too good. Gra**ce** and her trombone sounded like a sick moo**se**. Jill and her trumpet sounded like a flock of gee**se**.

The two of them made quite a racket.

It was so bad that Mister Spen**ce**r would yell, "I can't take it!" Then he would run out of the hou**se** and hide in the barn.

But, sin**ce** then, the children have gotten a lot better, just as Mister Van**ce** said they would. Mister Van**ce** is the band master. He spends a lot of time with the children, helping them get better.

In the spring there is a band concert in the park.

Mister Vance gets up on the bandstand and waves his hands. The band starts belting out a jazz song. They sound good. Grace hits the notes on her trumpet. Jill's trombone sounds good, too. The drummer is drumming up a storm. The band is **kn**ocking it out of the park.

Mister Vance has a big smile on his face. He is proud of Grace and Jill.

Mister Spencer smiles, too. He has gotten tired of spending so much time in the barn.

In the Storm Shelter

Directions: Have students reread the story and answer the questions.

1. Why are the Spencers down in the storm shelter?

   _____
   -
   _____
   -
   _____
   -
   _____
   -
   _____

   Page _____

2. What did Mister Spencer see when he peeked out from the storm shelter?

   _____
   -
   _____
   -
   _____
   -
   _____
   -
   _____

   Page _____

3. Describe what you do when it storms.

Spelling Test

1. _____

2. _____

3. _____

4. _____

5. _____

6. _____

7. _____

8. _____

Directions: Have students underline the plural marker in each word. Then have students write the plural words that end in /s/ under the /s/ header, the plural words that end in /z/ under the /z/ header, and the plural words that end in /ez/ under the /ez/ header:

cat<u>s</u>	<s>dogs</s>	<s>foxes</s>	sharks	forks
kids	dishes	porches	hands	crabs

/s/	/z/	/ez/

The Visit

Directions: Have students reread the story and answer the questions.

1. How do Grace and Jill feel in the car ride to visit their Gran?

   _____

   -

   _____

   _____

   -

   _____

   _____

   -

   _____

   Page _____

2. What do Grace and Jill do to get set to swim?

   _____

   -

   _____

   _____

   -

   _____

   _____

   -

   _____

   Page _____

3. Name three things Grace and Jill do with Gran.

Page _____

Dear Family Member,

Our class has been learning spelling alternatives for the /n/ sound. The /n/ sound can be written with the spellings 'n', 'nn', and 'kn'. The spelling words this week contain these spellings for /n/. As usual, there is one Tricky Word. Tricky Words do not play by the rules, meaning there are spellings that do not sound the way students would expect them to. These words need to be memorized, so your child will benefit from practice reading and writing them.

Spelling Words

1. knit

2. kneel

3. nose

4. center

5. nugget

6. running

7. winner

8. Tricky Word: which

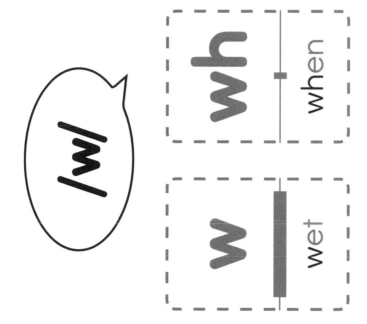

The Soccer Game

1. **Wh**y is Grace's soccer game this weekend such a big game?

   _____
   -
   _____
   _____
   -
   _____
   _____
   -
   _____

   Page _____

2. **Wh**y did Grace sit on the grass and pout?

   _____
   -
   _____
   _____
   -
   _____
   _____
   -
   _____

   Page _____

3. **Wh**at adv**ice** did Grace's dad tell Grace **wh**en she got upset?

_____

- - - - - - - - - - - - - - - - - - -

_____

- - - - - - - - - - - - - - - - - - -

_____

- - - - - - - - - - - - - - - - - - -

_____

- - - - - - - - - - - - - - - - - - -

_____

Page _____

4. **Wh**at happens at the end of the game?

_____

- - - - - - - - - - - - - - - - - - -

_____

- - - - - - - - - - - - - - - - - - -

_____

- - - - - - - - - - - - - - - - - - -

_____

- - - - - - - - - - - - - - - - - - -

_____

Page _____

Supper

1. **Wh**y are Kim and Jane **Kn**ox at Gra**ce**'s hou**se**?

   _____
   -
   _____
   -
   _____
   -
   _____

   Page _____

2. List the steps Gra**ce** takes to make the cake with her mom.

   _____
   -
   _____
   -
   _____
   -
   _____

   Page _____

3. If you had a supper at your hou**se**, **wh**at would you serve?

_____

– – – – – – – – – – – – – – – – –

_____

– – – – – – – – – – – – – – – – –

_____

– – – – – – – – – – – – – – – – –

_____

– – – – – – – – – – – – – – – – –

_____

– – – – – – – – – – – – – – – – –

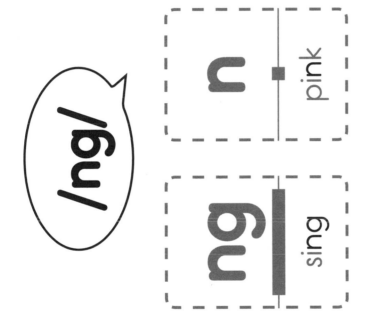

Name _____

Dear Family Member,

This is a story your child has probably read once, possibly several times, at school. Encourage your child to read the story to you and then talk about it together. The tricky parts in Tricky Words are underlined in gray.

Repeated oral reading is an important way to improve reading skills. It can be fun for your child to repeatedly read this story to a friend, relative, or even a pet.

The Visit

The Spencers are on a trip to visit their Gran. It's a long car ride from the farm. Their dad drives in the morning. Then their mom drives after lunch. Grace and Jill feel like the trip will never end.

At last, they get to Gran's place. Grace and Jill run up to their Gran and hug her.

"It's so nice to see you!" says Gran.

"Gran," Jill says, "can we run down and swim?" After the long car ride, the children need some exercise.

Gran smiles. She grabs her **kn**apsack and points to the flip-flops on her feet and says, "I'm all set!"

Grace and Jill get dressed for swimming. They rub sunscreen on their arms and legs. Mister Spencer helps them rub the sunscreen on their backs.

Once the sunscreen is on, Grace and Jill run down the path to the cove. When they get there, they wade in, yelping as the cool waves crash past them.

Grace and Jill splash and ride the waves. They dig for crabs and pick up shells. They toss a frisbee back and forth. They munch on snacks and sit in the sun. It's fun to visit with Gran.

Sound out the words with the lines under them. Is the 'n' sounded /n/ as in *nap* or /ng/ as in *pink*? Write in the words where they fit.

nap   1   ←   **n**   2 →   pink

fun   drink

nod   bank

	/n/ as in *nap*	/ng/ as in *pink*
1. I'm hot. Can I have something to dri**n**k?		drink
2. I can count to te**n**.		
3. I will not sell it to you, but I will le**n**d it to you.		
4. When will this e**n**d?		
5. I need some cash. Let's drive to the ba**n**k.		
6. I sat in the sun and got a ta**n**.		
7. At the park we can have lots of fu**n**.		
8. It is a nice gift. Tha**n**ks!		

Grace the Performer

1. **Wh**at is the job of a mime?

    _____

    -

    _____

    _____

    -

    _____

    _____

    -

    _____

    Page _____

2. **Wh**at tricks did Grace do to make the children smile?

    _____

    -

    _____

    _____

    -

    _____

    _____

    -

    _____

    Page _____

Directions: Have students reread the story and answer the questions.

3. **Wh**ich trick did you like best? **Wh**y?

_____

- - - - - - - - - - - - - - - - - - - -

_____

- - - - - - - - - - - - - - - - - - - -

_____

- - - - - - - - - - - - - - - - - - - -

_____

- - - - - - - - - - - - - - - - - - - -

_____

- - - - - - - - - - - - - - - - - - - -

Page _____

Name _____

Sort the words by their spellings for /ng/.

pink	long	drink	wing
sang	junk	jumping	bank
thing	finger	sting	singer

/ng/ → 'ng'   /ng/ → 'n'

_____   _____
- - - - - - - - - - - - -   - - - - - - - - - - - - -
_____   _____
- - - - - - - - - - - - -   - - - - - - - - - - - - -
_____   _____
- - - - - - - - - - - - -   - - - - - - - - - - - - -
_____   _____
- - - - - - - - - - - - -   - - - - - - - - - - - - -
_____   _____
- - - - - - - - - - - - -   - - - - - - - - - - - - -
_____   _____
- - - - - - - - - - - - -   - - - - - - - - - - - - -

Spelling Test

1. _____

2. _____

3. _____

4. _____

5. _____

6. _____

7. _____

8. _____

The Frog Jumping Contest

Directions: Have students reread the story and answer the questions.

1. **Wh**at are the names of Grace and Ken's frogs?

_____

- -

_____

_____

- -

_____

_____

- -

_____

Page _____

2. **Wh**at happened to Hopper at the start of the race?

_____

- -

_____

_____

- -

_____

_____

- -

_____

Page _____

3. **Wh**ich frog wins the race?

_____

‑ ‑

_____

‑ ‑

_____

‑ ‑

_____

‑ ‑

_____

Page _____

Can you see the spelling pattern? Fill in the chart.

Root Word	–ed Word	–ing Word
stop	stopped	stopping
munch		
sip		
kick		
fish		
slip		
dash		
wrap		

Can you see the spelling pattern? Fill in the chart.

Root Word	–ed Word	–ing Word
beg	begged	begging
tug		
flash		
park		
pat		
pin		

The Spinning Wheel

1. Describe the Spinning **Wh**eel.

_____

- - - - - - - - - - - - - - - - - - -

_____

- - - - - - - - - - - - - - - - - - -

_____

- - - - - - - - - - - - - - - - - - -

_____

   Page _____

2. **Wh**at did Grace dare Jill to do **wh**ile they rode the Spinning **Wh**eel?

_____

- - - - - - - - - - - - - - - - - - -

_____

- - - - - - - - - - - - - - - - - - -

_____

- - - - - - - - - - - - - - - - - - -

_____

   Page _____

3. **Wh**at el**se** do Grace and Jill do at the park?

_____

- - - - - - - - - - - - - - - - - - - -
_____

- - - - - - - - - - - - - - - - - - - -
_____

- - - - - - - - - - - - - - - - - - - -
_____

- - - - - - - - - - - - - - - - - - - -

Page _____

4. **Wh**y do Grace and Jill not ride the Spinning **Wh**eel two times?

_____

- - - - - - - - - - - - - - - - - - - -
_____

- - - - - - - - - - - - - - - - - - - -
_____

- - - - - - - - - - - - - - - - - - - -
_____

- - - - - - - - - - - - - - - - - - - -

Page _____

Name _____

Dear Family Member,

This is a story your child has probably read once, possibly several times, at school. Encourage your child to read the story to you and then talk about it together. The tricky parts in Tricky Words are underlined in gray.

Repeated oral reading is an important way to improve reading skills. It can be fun for your child to repeatedly read this story to a friend, relative, or even a pet.

The Frog Jumping Contest

There is a frog jumping contest at the park this week, too.

"Did you get a frog for the contest?" Ken asks. Grace nods. She sticks her hand in her bag and grabs her frog. The frog sits on her fingers.

"Cool!" Ken says. "What's his name?"

"It's a she!" says Grace. "Her name is Hopper."

"I got one, too," says Ken. "His name is Legs." Legs has longer legs than Hopper.

Grace and Ken take their frogs to the starting line. They set the frogs down. The starter shouts, "On your mark! Get set! Hop!"

"Jump!" Ken yells. "Jump!" Legs hops off.

Hopper jumps, too, but she jumps off to the side.

"No, Hopper!" Grace yells. She runs and grabs her frog. Then she sets her down with her face pointing at the finish line.

Hopper hops off. This time she is lined up and on target.

Ken and Grace chase their frogs down the track. The frogs are fast. It is a close race.

The two frogs cross the finish line at the same time.

"Did Legs win?" Ken asks.

"Did Hopper win?" Grace asks.

"We have two winners!" says the man at the finish line. "Hopper and Legs crossed the line at the same time. They will share the prize!"

The man hands Grace and Ken a cup for their prize. Grace plops Hopper in the cup. Ken adds Legs. Then they hoist the cup up and shout, "Here's to the champs!"

Buster the Pig

1. **Wh**at is a livestock contest?

Page _____

2. **Wh**y is Rod grooming Buster?

Page _____

Directions: Have students reread the story and answer the questions.

3. **Wh**o inspects the pigs? **Wh**at is his job?

Page _____

4. **Wh**ich pig wins the prize?

Page _____

Write the words on the correct lines.

1. prin**ce**   

_____   _____

- - - - - - - - - - - - - - - -   - - - - - - - - - - - - - - - -

_____   _____

2. mou**se**    

_____   _____

- - - - - - - - - - - - - - - -   - - - - - - - - - - - - - - - -

_____   _____

3. dan**ce**r    

_____   _____

- - - - - - - - - - - - - - - -   - - - - - - - - - - - - - - - -

_____   _____

4. rin**se**   

_____   _____

- - - - - - - - - - - - - - - -   - - - - - - - - - - - - - - - -

_____   _____

5. **kn**ot   

_____   _____

- - - - - - - - - - - - - - - -   - - - - - - - - - - - - - - - -

_____   _____

6. finger

_____

- - - - - - - - - - -

_____

7. **kn**it

_____

- - - - - - - - - - -

_____

8. **wh**ale

_____

- - - - - - - - - - -

_____

9. **c**ent

_____

- - - - - - - - - - -

_____

10. boun**ce**

_____

- - - - - - - - - - -

_____

Directions: For each word, have students circle and count the spellings, then write the number of sounds in the box and copy the word on the lines.

1. **kn**ob

2. **wh**iskers

3. choi**ce**

4. bli**n**k

5. **c**ent

6. glan**ce**

7. grou**se**

8. hitch

9. hu**n**ger

10. thi**n**k

11. hou**se**

12. **wh**ale

13. **wh**isper

14. **kn**ocking

15. **c**ells

16. magic

Whisper

Directions: Have students reread the story and answer the questions.

1. **Wh**at can wool be used for?

Page _____

2. **Wh**y did Grace ask to bring a chick home?

Page _____

3. **Wh**at are some of the name choices Grace gets from her mom, dad, and Jill?

Page _____

4. Describe a pet you have or would like to have.

Name _____

Dear Family Member,

   Please have your child read the sentence and circle the correct pronoun for the underlined noun or noun phrase.

1. <u>Sam and Pat</u> ran a race.

    a. We   b. She   c. They

2. <u>Jim</u> is **kn**itting a scarf for me.

    a. We   b. He   c. It

3. <u>Mom and Dad</u> went dancing.

    a. She   b. They   c. We

4. <u>The mou**se**</u> ran and hid.

    a. It   b. He   c. We

5. <u>Kate</u> dressed up like a princess.

    a. They   b. She   c. We

6. <u>Jake and I</u> solved the math problem.

    a. We   b. He   c. They

Mark the words that are said.

1.	blouse	bound	bounce	pounce
2.	moose	mouse	nice	mice
3.	long	link	like	lick
4.	wipe	wilt	wind	whip
5.	tense	fence	ten	twice
6.	plaster	perch	percent	partner
7.	note	knot	cot	knock
8.	wage	wake	waste	whack
9.	nine	wife	knave	knife
10.	sing	sink	simmer	since

The Harvest

1. **Wh**o helps Mister Spencer bring in the harvest?

    _____

    _____

    _____

    _____

    Page _____

2. **Wh**at do combines do?

    _____

    _____

    _____

    _____

    Page _____

Directions: Have students reread the story and answer the questions.

3. **Wh**at did Hank spot on the ground?

_____

- - - - - - - - - - - - - - - - - - - -

_____

- - - - - - - - - - - - - - - - - - - -

_____

- - - - - - - - - - - - - - - - - - - -

_____

- - - - - - - - - - - - - - - - - - - -

_____

Page _____

4. **Wh**ere do you thi**nk** the relic is from? Draw a
   pic<u>ture</u> to help you describe the tale of the relic.

_____

- - - - - - - - - - - - - - - - - - - -

_____

- - - - - - - - - - - - - - - - - - - -

_____

- - - - - - - - - - - - - - - - - - - -

_____

```
┌─────────────────────────────────────┐
│                                       │
│                                       │
│                                       │
│                                       │
│                                       │
│                                       │
└─────────────────────────────────────┘
```

The Prince Gets a Pet

Once there was a prin**ce** named Francis. Prin**ce** Francis was ni**ce**, but he sometimes did things without thi**n**king.

One morning Prin**ce** Francis felt sad. He went to see his sister, Prin**c**ess Rose.

"I'm sad," he said. "**Wh**at can I do to make myself feel better?"

"You sh**ou**ld get a pet," said his sister. "**Wh**en I feel sad, I visit with my cat. Then I feel better."

"A pet!" said Prin**ce** Francis. "I like the sound of that." He shouted to his men, "Bring me my hor**se**! I will ride out and look for a pet!"

So Prin**ce** Francis rode out to look for a pet. After a bit, he saw a sku**n**k. He had never seen a sku**n**k.

"Look at that cat!" he said. "I have never seen a cat like that! He's black with a ni**ce** **wh**ite stripe on his back. He will be the perfect pet for me!"

The prince jumped off his horse and ran up to grab the skunk. His men shouted at him to stop, but it was too late.

The skunk made a big stink.

The prince ran back to his horse. "Yuck!" he shouted, "I stink!" His men nodded. He did stink.

The prince rode home. When he got back, the princess helped him rinse off the stink. She said, "Francis, that was not a cat. That was a skunk. Skunks do not make good pets. Let me pick a pet for you. I have one that will be perfect."

The princess went and got a goose. "This is a nice goose," she said. "She is soft, she will not bite, and she smells much better than a skunk."

The prince liked the goose, and the goose liked him. It was the perfect pet.

The Prince Gets a Pet

1. Francis is _____.

    ○   a prin**c**ess

    ○   a prin**ce**

    ○   a cat

    ○   a hor**se**

2. Rose is _____.

    ○   a prin**c**ess

    ○   a prin**ce**

    ○   a sku**n**k

    ○   a hor**se**

3. **Wh**at did Rose tell Fran**c**is he sh<u>ou</u>ld get?

    ○   She said he sh<u>ou</u>ld get a pig.

    ○   She said he sh<u>ou</u>ld get a sku**n**k.

    ○   She said he sh<u>ou</u>ld get a hor**se**.

    ○   She said he sh<u>ou</u>ld get a pet.

4. Francis saw something that was black with a **wh**ite stripe. **Wh**at was it?

   - ○ It was a cat.
   - ○ It was a hor**se**.
   - ○ It was a sku**n**k.
   - ○ It was a chipmu**n**k.

5. **Wh**y did Francis need to be rin**se**d off **wh**en he got back?

   - ○ He was hot.
   - ○ A sku**n**k made him sti**n**k.
   - ○ He fell off his hor**se** and skinned his **kn**ee.
   - ○ He fell in the mud.

6. **Wh**at pet did Rose pick for Francis in the end?

   - ○ She picked a cat.
   - ○ She picked a sku**n**k.
   - ○ She picked a goo**se**.
   - ○ She picked a dog.

7. It says, "Prin**ce** Fran**c**is was ni**ce**, but he sometimes did things without thi**n**king . . ."

   What was the *biggest* thing Prince Fran**c**is did without thi**n**king in this tale?

   ○ He asked his sister for advi**ce**.

   ○ He grabbed a critter he had never seen and got covered in sti**n**k.

   ○ He and his men rode out to look for a pet.

   ○ He let his sister help him get a pet.

8. **Wh**y did Prince Francis think the goose was a perfect pet?

   ○ He can pet the soft goose and it does not smell bad.

   ○ He could tell the goose **wh**y he feels sad.

   ○ The goose can make eggs.

   ○ The goose looks better than a skunk.

The Harvest Marvel

1. **Wh**en do the Spencers have a Harvest Fest?

   _____

   -

   _____

   _____

   -

   _____

   _____

   -

   _____

   Page _____

2. **Wh**o did Mister Spencer tell the kids to look out for?

   _____

   -

   _____

   _____

   -

   _____

   _____

   -

   _____

   Page _____

Directions: Have students reread the story and answer the questions.

3. **Wh**at did the Harvest Marvel look like?

_____

Page _____

4. **Wh**y did Grace thin**k** the Harvest Marvel was Ha**n**k?

_____

Page _____

Cut out the word cards and stick them on Worksheet PP2.

cell

center

voi**ce**

prin**ce**

twi**ce**

el**se**

den**se**

chan**ce**

hou**se**

hor**se**

per**c**ent

dan**c**ing

Sort the word cards from Worksheet PP1 by their spellings for /s/ and stick them in the boxes.

/s/ → 'se'						
/s/ → 'c' or 'ce'						

Cut out the word cards and stick them on Worksheet PP4.

knife	napkin
number	**kn**obs
knees	nice
notch	**kn**ocked
muffin	**kn**eeling
knitting	nest

Sort the word cards from Worksheet PP3 by their spellings for /n/ and stick them in the boxes.

/n/ → 'kn'	/n/ → 'n'

Cut out the word cards and stick them on Worksheet PP6.

thi**n**k	feeling
string	dri**n**k
hopping	wrong
finger	fling
sti**n**k	pi**n**k
singer	hunger

Sort the word cards from Worksheet PP5 by their spellings for /ng/ and stick them in the boxes.

/ng/ → 'ng'	/ng/ → 'n'

Cut out the word cards and stick them on Worksheet PP8.

why

were

waves

whimper

whisk

where

winter

twelve

wake

whale

white

weeks

Sort the word cards from Worksheet PP7 by their spellings for /w/ and stick them in the boxes.

/w/ → 'wh'	/w/ → 'w'

Cut out the word cards and stick them on Worksheet PP10.

buzz	fuzz
zoom	buzzing
farmers	prize
jazz	cars
things	freezer
homes	zipper

Sort the word cards from Worksheet PP9 by their spellings for /z/ and stick them in the boxes.

/z/ → 's'						
/z/ → 'zz'						
/z/ → 'z'						

Sort the words by their spellings for /s/.

| dance | bounce | blouse | prince | fence |
| rinse | voice | geese | dense | force |

/s/ → 'ce'

_____

- - - - - - - - - - - - - - - - - -

_____

_____

- - - - - - - - - - - - - - - - - -

_____

_____

- - - - - - - - - - - - - - - - - -

_____

_____

- - - - - - - - - - - - - - - - - -

_____

_____

- - - - - - - - - - - - - - - - - -

_____

/s/ → 'se'

_____

- - - - - - - - - - - - - - - - - -

_____

_____

- - - - - - - - - - - - - - - - - -

_____

_____

- - - - - - - - - - - - - - - - - -

_____

_____

- - - - - - - - - - - - - - - - - -

_____

_____

- - - - - - - - - - - - - - - - - -

_____

Directions: Have students color the boxes that contain words that have 'n' > /n/ as in nap in one color and the boxes that contain words that have 'n' > /ng/ as in pink in another color.

stink	trunk	wren
nest	plank	fence
longest	drink	green
chunks	snatch	notch

Mark the words that are said. Then write them on the lines.

1. fen**ce**   fetch   _____

2. moo**se**   mou**se**   _____

3. dri**nk**   dra**nk**   _____

4. **wh**isker   wither   _____

5. **c**ent   **c**enter   _____

6. dan**c**er   dander   _____

7. **kn**ock   not   _____

8. **kn**ee   need   _____

9. ba**nk**   bla**nk**   _____

10. ten**se**   den**se**   _____

Yes or no? Write *yes* or *no* on the lines.

1. Is a **kn**ife sharp?   _____

2. Do snakes have **wh**iskers?   _____

3. Can a mou**se** write with a
   pen?   _____

4. Can you feel your pul**se**?   _____

5. Is a quilt like a bla**n**ket?   _____

6. Is pepper a spi**ce**?   _____

7. Do you have a loud voi**ce**?   _____

8. Do you like to dan**ce**?   _____

9. Do you have a bu**n**k bed?

10. Is ten **c**ents less than a dime?

11. Is an **ic**eberg made of **ic**e?

12. Is ri**ce** a food?

13. Do sku**n**ks smell good?

14. Can a hor**se** run fast?

15. Do cars have six **wh**eels?

16. Can a **wh**ale jump rope?

In the box are six words. Write them on the correct lines.

knitting   **kn**ot   nap

dinner   **kn**ee   nine

_____

_ _ _ _ _ _ _ _ _

_____

_____

_ _ _ _ _ _ _ _ _

_____

In the box are six words. Write them on the correct lines.

whiskers	wave	web
whale	**wh**eel	weep

_____

- - - - - - - - - - - - - - - - - -

_____

_____

- - - - - - - - - - - - - - - - - -

_____

In the box are six words. Write them on the correct lines.

| finger | sing | sink |
| drink | ring | skunk |

_____
- - - - - - - - - - -
_____

_____
- - - - - - - - - - -
_____

_____
- - - - - - - - - - -
_____

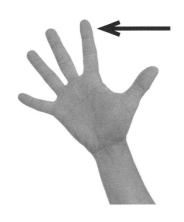

_____
- - - - - - - - - - -
_____

_____
- - - - - - - - - - -
_____

_____
- - - - - - - - - - -
_____

Name _____

Write the words on the correct lines.

1. **kn**ife

_____

_____

2. bla**n**ket

_____

_____

3. hou**se**

_____

_____

4. **c**ent

_____

_____

5. fen**ce**

_____

_____

6. goo**se**

7. **kn**eel

8. li**n**ks

9. **wh**isper

10. **wh**eel

Fill in the gaps.

                               _____

1. I baked muffins _____ you were sleeping.

       _____

2. _____ your mouth well after brushing your teeth.

                 _____

3. Who is _____ their horn like that?

                           _____

4. I made that mistake _____!

                   _____

5. This is a short _____.

                     _____

6. Do you like to _____ ?

                 _____

7. I have a soft _____ on my bed.

                        _____

8. This tree has a thick _____.

Plan

_____
- - - - - - - - - - - - - - - -
_____

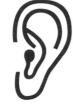

Draft

I will describe

Ending
Sentence

Directions: Have students complete the individual parts of the draft based on Worksheet PP19. Have students write complete sentences.

Directions: Have students write the nouns that the underlined pronouns replace on the lines.

1. Jim went to France. <u>He</u> has a pal there.

    Jim

2. Francis said, "<u>I</u> saw a goose outside."

3. Jen has a **kn**it hat. <u>It</u> itches.

4. Gran said, "Kate, can <u>you</u> hand me the coin?"

5. Deb has a dress. <u>She</u> likes it.

6. Dan and Sam said, "<u>We</u> plunged into the pool."

7. Marge and Jim got a dog. <u>They</u> are glad.

Add 's' or 'es' to the gaps based on the word.

1. Ants make anthill_____.

2. My pal Tom has three bike_____.

3. I have fifteen classmate_____.

4. Our cat had two litter_____.

5. A tree has lots of branch_____.

6. I do not like to take pill_____.

7. In the park are a lot of bench_____ to sit on.

8. My mom has five summer dress_____.

Dear Family Member,

This is a story your child has probably read once, possibly several times, at school. Encourage your child to read the story to you and then talk about it together. The tricky parts in Tricky Words are underlined in gray.

Repeated oral reading is an important way to improve reading skills. It can be fun for your child to repeatedly read this story to a friend, relative, or even a pet.

The Spinning Wheel

There are lots of fun rides and games at the park this week. Gra**c**e and Jill like to ride the Spinning **Wh**eel. The Spinning **Wh**eel is a ride with six arms. The arms spin round and round and lift up. It is fun to ride.

"Jill!" Gra**c**e yells as the **wh**eel starts to spin, "I dare you to keep your hands up **wh**ile you ride, like this!"

Soon they are **wh**izzing and **wh**ooshing and shouting and yelling. Gra**c**e keeps her hands up till the ride ends. Jill keeps her hands up for a **wh**ile, but not all the time.

"**Wh**oo-hoo!" shouts Gra**c**e.

"**Wh**ook at me!" shouts Jill. Her cheeks are pi**n**k with ex**c**itement.

When they get off the Spinning **Wh**eel, they run and check out the games. Gra**c**e shoots hoops **wh**ile Jill tosses darts at a target. Jill wins a prize!

"Let's have a snack!" says Gra**c**e. The sisters get a big tub of buttered popcorn. They share a corn dog and a dri**n**k, too. The food is good.

When they are finished, Jill asks, "Sh<u>ou</u>ld we ride the Spinning **Wh**eel one last time?"

"No," Gra**c**e says. "After all that food, it would not be safe. I thi**n**k I would get sick!"

Dear Family Member,

This is a story your child has probably read once, possibly several times, at school. Encourage your child to read the story to you and then talk about it together. The tricky parts in Tricky Words are underlined in gray.

Repeated oral reading is an important way to improve reading skills. It can be fun for your child to repeatedly read this story to a friend, relative, or even a pet.

Buster the Pig

There are also contests at the park besides games and rides. Grace is at a livestock contest with her dad. **Wh**en a livestock contest is held, farmers bring their best sheep and pigs and hope to win a prize.

"Look at the size of that p**i**n**k** pig!" Grace says.

"His name is Buster," says a teen in a **wh**ite ta**n**k standing next to the pig. He is rubbing the pig's fla**nk** with a rag. "And my name is Rod."

"**Wh**at are you doing to him?" Grace asks.

"I'm grooming him," says Rod. "Buster needs to look his best so he can win the top prize. Would you like to help?"

When it's time to take Buster out into the ring, Grace rubs him under his chin. Buster likes this so much he oi**n**ks and **wh**impers.

There are lots of pigs in the ring, and they all look good. A man in a black hat inspects the pigs. His job is to pick **wh**ich pig he thi**n**ks is best. That pig will be the winner.

"I hope Buster wins!" Grace says.

The man looks at the pigs one last time. Then he points a fi**n**ger at Buster and hands the top prize to Rod.

"Yippee!" says Grace. "Buster is number one!"

Dear Family Member,

This is a story your child has probably read once, possibly several times, at school. Encourage your child to read the story to you and then talk about it together. The tricky parts in Tricky Words are underlined in gray.

Repeated oral reading is an important way to improve reading skills. It can be fun for your child to repeatedly read this story to a friend, relative, or even a pet.

Whisper

Grace and Jill like to visit the livestock contest. There are lots of fun things to do there.

In one barn, they see a man cutting wool off a sheep. They feel the wool the man has cut from the sheep. It is soft. The man tells them that the wool can be used to **kn**it hats and scarves and mittens.

Jill gets to milk a <u>cow</u>. She likes to see the milk shoot out of the udder and splash in the bucket.

Grace picks up a rabbit. The rabbit is cute with lots of fuzz.

Then Grace sees chicks that have just hatched out of their eggs! She picks one up and pets it. She thi**n**ks the chick is the softest thing she has ever petted.

"Are the chicks for sale?" she asks.

"Yep," says the man.

"Can I bring this one home?" Grace asks. She looks at her mom and dad.

"It's fine with me," says her dad. "But you have to take good care of her."

"I will, I will!" says Grace.

Mister Spencer hands the man some cash. The man plops the chick in a box and hands Grace the box.

In the car, Grace asks, "**Wh**at sh**ould** I name her?"

"Snickers!" says Jill.

"**Wh**izbang!" says Mom.

"Gem!" says Dad.

"No," says Grace. "I will name her **Wh**isper!"

Name _____

Dear Family Member,

This is a story your child has probably read once, possibly several times, at school. Encourage your child to read the story to you and then talk about it together.

Repeated oral reading is an important way to improve reading skills. It can be fun for your child to repeatedly read this story to a friend, relative, or even a pet.

The Harvest

Mister Spencer must harvest his corn **wh**en it is ripe. He can't let it spoil. It's a big job. Sometimes he has to hire helpers to help him bring in the harvest.

Grace likes two of the helpers her dad hires. Their names are Hank and **C**edric. **Wh**en they finish twelfth grade, they plan to be farmers like Mister Spen**c**er.

Mister Spen**c**er gets out his big combine and fills the tank with gas. Then he starts it up. It sends up a puff of black smoke. The combine is loud. But it is good at cutting down corn.

Mister Spencer drives the combine in the morning. After lunch, he lets **Ha**n**k** and **C**edric drive. They drive the combine back and forth until all of the corn is cut down. **Gra**c**e** rides with them part of the time.

When they are finished with the harvest, Han**k** spots **wh**at looks like a rock sticking up out of the ground. He bends down and grabs it.

"**Wh**at is it?" **C**edric asks.

"I thi**n**k it's a chu**n**k of a pot," says Han**k**. He dusts it off with his fi**n**gers and says, "It could be a relic from a long time back in the past!"

Back at the hou**se**, Han**k** hands the pot shard to **Gra**c**e**. "Here," he says. "This is for you. We can't tell, but we thi**n**k it could be a relic."

"Thanks!" says **Gra**c**e**, with a smile. Then she runs to get Han**k** and **C**edric some corn muffins. They sit on the steps and munch on the muffins.

Name _____

Dear Family Member,

This is a story your child has probably read once, possibly several times, at school. Encourage your child to read the story to you and then talk about it together.

Repeated oral reading is an important way to improve reading skills. It can be fun for your child to repeatedly read this story to a friend, relative, or even a pet.

The Harvest Marvel

After the harvest, the Spencers had a Harvest Fest on their farm. A bunch of children came.

"Have fun!" Mister Spencer said to the children. "And look out for the Harvest Marvel!"

"What's the Harvest Marvel?" one of the children asked.

"There is a legend that farmers have passed down for a long time. At the Harvest Fest, someone dresses as the Harvest Marvel to celebrate all of the crops and good food we harvest in the fall. It's a tribute to thank the Harvest Marvel for the harvest. But who or what the Harvest Marvel is can be the best game at the Harvest Fest!" said Mister Spencer.

The children pondered this for a bit and then skipped off to get snacks and drinks. Time passed, and they had forgotten to look out for the Harvest Marvel—until something

or someone stepped out of the darkness next to the barn. It was hard to tell what it was. Its arms and legs were wrapped in corn husks. It had a pumpkin on its face as a mask.

"Greetings!" shouted the Harvest Marvel, jumping up and down. The children did not recognize the voice of the Harvest Marvel, and could not tell who or what the Harvest Marvel was.

They were spooked and started to run.

Grace started to run from the Harvest Marvel, too. But then she spotted a jacket on the Harvest Marvel, under the corn husks. She recognized that jacket.

Grace ran up to the Harvest Marvel and tagged it. By accident, she knocked the pumpkin mask off of the Harvest Marvel.

"See!" Grace yelled. "It's just Hank!"

When the children saw that the Harvest Marvel was just Hank, they ran up and jumped on top of him. Hank and the children were all smiles.

The Jumping Fish

1. **Wh**ere are Grace and Jill?

_____
- - - - - - - - - - - - - - - - -
_____
_____
- - - - - - - - - - - - - - - - -
_____
_____
- - - - - - - - - - - - - - - - -
_____

Page _____

2. Describe **wh**at the big, green fish did.

_____
- - - - - - - - - - - - - - - - -
_____
_____
- - - - - - - - - - - - - - - - -
_____
_____
- - - - - - - - - - - - - - - - -
_____

Page _____

Directions: Have students reread the story and answer the questions.

3. **Wh**y did Grace's mom think the fish was jumping next to them?

_____

- -

_____

- -

_____

- -

_____

- -

_____

Page _____

4. **Wh**y did Jill think the fish was jumping next to them?

_____

- -

_____

- -

_____

- -

_____

- -

_____

Page _____

Snakes

1. How did Grace start her speech?

_____
- - - - - - - - - - - - - - - - - -
_____

- - - - - - - - - - - - - - - - - -
_____

- - - - - - - - - - - - - - - - - -
_____

- - - - - - - - - - - - - - - - - -
_____

Page _____

2. **Wh**at happens **wh**en snakes get too big for their outside skin?

_____
- - - - - - - - - - - - - - - - - -
_____

- - - - - - - - - - - - - - - - - -
_____

- - - - - - - - - - - - - - - - - -
_____

- - - - - - - - - - - - - - - - - -
_____

Page _____

Directions: Have students reread the story and answer the questions.

3. **Wh**at happens **wh**en a snake catches a mou**se**?

Page _____

4. **Wh**y is it not safe to grab a snake?

Page _____

CORE KNOWLEDGE LANGUAGE ARTS

SERIES EDITOR-IN-CHIEF
E. D. Hirsch, Jr.

PRESIDENT
Linda Bevilacqua

EDITORIAL STAFF
Carolyn Gosse, Senior Editor - Preschool
Khara Turnbull, Materials Development Manager
Michelle L. Warner, Senior Editor - Listening & Learning

Mick Anderson
Robin Blackshire
Maggie Buchanan
Paula Coyner
Sue Fulton
Sara Hunt
Erin Kist
Robin Luecke
Rosie McCormick
Cynthia Peng
Liz Pettit
Ellen Sadler
Deborah Samley
Diane Auger Smith
Sarah Zelinke

DESIGN AND GRAPHICS STAFF
Scott Ritchie, Creative Director

Kim Berrall
Michael Donegan
Liza Greene
Matt Leech
Bridget Moriarty
Lauren Pack

CONSULTING PROJECT MANAGEMENT SERVICES
ScribeConcepts.com

ADDITIONAL CONSULTING SERVICES
Ang Blanchette
Dorrit Green
Carolyn Pinkerton

ACKNOWLEDGMENTS

These materials are the result of the work, advice, and encouragement of numerous individuals over many years. Some of those singled out here already know the depth of our gratitude; others may be surprised to find themselves thanked publicly for help they gave quietly and generously for the sake of the enterprise alone. To helpers named and unnamed we are deeply grateful.

CONTRIBUTORS TO EARLIER VERSIONS OF THESE MATERIALS
Susan B. Albaugh, Kazuko Ashizawa, Nancy Braier, Kathryn M. Cummings, Michelle De Groot, Diana Espinal, Mary E. Forbes, Michael L. Ford, Ted Hirsch, Danielle Knecht, James K. Lee, Diane Henry Leipzig, Martha G. Mack, Liana Mahoney, Isabel McLean, Steve Morrison, Juliane K. Munson, Elizabeth B. Rasmussen, Laura Tortorelli, Rachael L. Shaw, Sivan B. Sherman, Miriam E. Vidaver, Catherine S. Whittington, Jeannette A. Williams

We would like to extend special recognition to Program Directors Matthew Davis and Souzanne Wright who were instrumental to the early development of this program.

SCHOOLS
We are truly grateful to the teachers, students, and administrators of the following schools for their willingness to field test these materials and for their invaluable advice: Capitol View Elementary, Challenge Foundation Academy (IN), Community Academy Public Charter School, Lake Lure Classical Academy, Lepanto Elementary School, New Holland Core Knowledge Academy, Paramount School of Excellence, Pioneer Challenge Foundation Academy, New York City PS 26R (The Carteret School), PS 30X (Wilton School), PS 50X (Clara Barton School), PS 96Q, PS 102X (Joseph O. Loretan), PS 104Q (The Bays Water), PS 214K (Michael Friedsam), PS 223Q (Lyndon B. Johnson School), PS 308K (Clara Cardwell), PS 333Q (Goldie Maple Academy), Sequoyah Elementary School, South Shore Charter Public School, Spartanburg Charter School, Steed Elementary School, Thomas Jefferson Classical Academy, Three Oaks Elementary, West Manor Elementary.

And a special thanks to the CKLA Pilot Coordinators Anita Henderson, Yasmin Lugo-Hernandez, and Susan Smith, whose suggestions and day-to-day support to teachers using these materials in their classrooms was critical.

CREDITS